DOMENICO SCARLATTI

THE SCHOLAR'S
SCARLATTI

A GRADED PROGRESSION OF 42 SONATAS THROUGH STYLE AND TECHNIQUE

SELECTED AND EDITED BY STODDARD LINCOLN

VOLUME THREE

WITH A TABLE OF SIGNS AND ORNAMENTS,
AND NOTES ON THE INDIVIDUAL SONATAS

GW00646610

NOVELLO PUBLISHING LIMITED
8/9 Frith Street, London W1V 5TZ

Order No: NOV 100275

Contents

Foreword

Stoddard Lincoln, who holds the highest degrees from the Julliard School of Music in performance and from Oxford University in music history, is the Dirctor of Graduate Studies at the Conservatory of Music at Brooklyn College and a Professor of Music on the Doctoral Faculty at the City University of New York. As a performer on both harpsichord and fortepiano he spends much time giving public concerts, coaching early music ensembles and lecturing. He has been a critic for *The Financial Times* (London) and is a staff reviewer for *Stereo-Review* where he specialises in writing about the early music scene.

His collection of Scarlatti sonatas combines excellent yet generally unfamiliar pieces with thorough technical and stylistic analyses. The sonatas have been chosen according to four criteria: the range of technical problems they present; the variety of styles and forms they contain; their musical quality; and their rarity (many being generally unavailable unless one purchases the complete works).

Professor Lincoln has also grouped the sonatas into Sets according to key. Each Set includes many different technical problems but also makes a satisfying musical unit for performance. Preceding each Set is a detailed commentary on the sonatas in the group, analysing the technical problems encountered, and suggesting approaches to the interpretation of each sonata. These commentaries on individual Sets are amplified by an extensive, informative Preface (only in Volume One), and a Table of signs and ornaments (to be found in each volume).

Table of signs and ornaments

Notes with dots over them are to be played detached or staccato.

Notes under a slur are to be overlapped.

All other notes are played legato, i.e. joined but not overlapped. They may be imperceptibly detached in brilliant passages.

Square brackets indicate phrases and are to be taken with one rising-wrist motion.

Commas indicate articulations and are to be made with the fingers only within the rising-wrist motion of the phrase.

Appoggiaturas are slurred to the note they precede, i.e. the two notes are overlapped. All appoggiaturas are taken on the beat, and the time value, indicated by the appoggiatura itself, is to be subtracted from the note of resolution. The duration of an appoggiatura may be lengthened or shortened at the discretion of the player.

Acciaccaturas are indicated by a grace note with a slash through it. They are to be played as quickly as possible if not 'smashed', i.e. played simultaneously with the note they precede.

The short trill (⤳) is taken on the beat, not before, and takes less than the value of the note when possible so that there is a pause before the next note. It may begin on the principal note or the upper auxiliary at the discretion of the player. The fingering will suggest the editor's preference. If the short trill is preceded by a grace note above it, the trill *must* begin on the upper auxiliary. All such grace notes are Scarlatti's, not the editor's.

The long trill (**tr**) is also taken on the beat but lasts the entire value of the note and ends with a turn, i.e. the last note of the trill will be one note lower than the trill and will go directly without pause to the next note. They too may begin on the principal note or upper auxiliary (editorial preference indicated by the fingering) unless preceded by a grace note on the upper auxiliary. Short and long trills are interchangeable at the player's discretion unless there is a written termination (Scarlatti's, not the editor's), in which case a long trill with the written termination *must* be used.

For a fuller explanation of the above, see the editor's *Preface* in Volume One. Details concerning specific passages are found in the editor's commentary that precedes each set.

Notes on the individual sonatas: Volume Three

In Volumes One and Two of *The Scholar's Scarlatti* the choice of the sonatas was dictated primarily by their technical content: they were arranged into sets which became increasingly difficult. Even though the six pairs of sonatas in Volume Three also continue to get progressively more difficult and will bring your technique to a high peak, the choice has been made more on musical grounds than on technical considerations. Volume Three is, so to speak, your reward for the hard work you have put into the first two volumes. After you have conquered them you should be able to attack any Scarlatti sonata you wish, confidently knowing that you will be able to come to grips with its technical problems, fingering, phrasing and articulation. You should also be able to make intelligent decisions concerning the auxiliaries and terminations of trills and the length of appoggiaturas.

Thanks to the researches of Ralph Kirkpatrick it is now generally believed that many of Scarlatti's sonatas were played in pairs. I have followed that theory in the presentation of six pairs in Volume Three. In choosing pairs the only criteria are that the two sonatas must be in the same key and be contrasting in their mood, usually a lyric sonata followed by a more brilliant one. If the 'K' numbers are consecutive in this volume the pair was selected by Kirkpatrick. Pairs with disjunct numbers are of my own choice. There is no reason why you cannot choose your own pairs from the three volumes of this collection as long as you follow the criteria of key and mood.

Set 1 in E Major
31. K. 162 (L. 121)

The form of this sonata with its sharply-contrasting moods is curious. One would expect the second section to be in the same form as the first, i.e. a return to the *Andante* immediately after the double bar. Scarlatti, always full of surprises, opts to continue with the *Allegro* across the double bar before returning to the *Andante* after which he brings the piece to a brilliant close. The form becomes even more asymetrical when the repeats are taken. The first repeat, incidentally, goes back to the very beginning, not to the beginning of the *Allegro*.

Notice that in the *Andante* section the second and third beats are almost always slurred. When the second beat is a dissonance and resolves to a consonance on the third beat, linger slightly on the second beat. This is particularly true of bars 16-19. Savour the second beat the most in bar 18 for the unexpected shift to the minor mode.

In bars 7-10 the second and third beats do not sound well slurred because of the ornaments. In these bars articulate the second and third beats just a trifle. The fingering will encourage you to do this.

At the end of each of the *Allegro* sections Scarlatti repeats little motifs several times in a row. Jab at them, like a dog playing with a bone. The effect can be quite amusing.

bb 49–50 The purpose of the long trill here is to create a lunge into the demi-semiquaver slides. Be sure to play the dots as rests here so that each demi-semiquaver jab will be articulated. Two lines down he will really take this figure for a whirl.

b 55 The last beat of the original has an E rather than F sharp. Considering the left hand of the surrounding bars, it should be F sharp to make a consistent sequence.

bb 83–89 Watch the staccatos in the left hand very carefully as they are quite irregular, especially in bar 84 where they shift from the weak beat to the strong beat. In order to bring out the staccato you might try slurring the notes which are not staccato.

bb 90–2 Don't even think about the wild leap between the 4th and 5th fingers in the left hand. Just practise it like this:

EXAMPLE 1

32. K. 162 (L. 63)

This delicate sonata is a study in sophisticated articulation. Even though one manuscript bears the tempo *Allegro*, the source on which this edition is based bears no tempo mark. *Allegretto* is certainly as fast as one can manage it gracefully. The key of E Major will keep you on top of the keys with a high wrist, but that is no excuse not to phrase.

The many cross-overs in the fingering are designed to bring out the articulation, if not to make it impossible to ignore it. For example, crossing the 3rd finger over the 4th in bars 3 and 4 keeps the wrist up for the end of the phrase and makes it impossible to come down with a thump on the side of your hand, which you would if you used your thumb on the B and ended up on E with the little finger. Study the staccato markings with care as they give the sonata its character.

bb 17 & 18 Hasten the triplets a bit so that you can hold the high B slightly to give this passage the lilt it deserves. The passage is ubiquitous so experiment with it. Keep the rocking left hand very legato, even slurred if you wish.

bb 23–4 The skip from F sharp to B in the left hand 5th finger can be hazardous. If you hold the F sharp on the first beat with your thumb until the beginning of the next bar, it will not only stabilize your hand so that you can measure the leap with the little finger, but it will also keep the sound going so the break caused by the jumping little finger is not obvious. Watch for this in bars 31–2 and 55–6.

bb 53–4 In the original the D natural is tied over to where the C sharp now stands and the C sharp is missing: certainly a mistake as the D natural cries out to be resolved to C sharp.

bb 61–4 The high D natural is the climax of the piece because it is preceded by the widest leap in the sonata and is also the highest note. Treat it specially by beginning the measure with a little ritardando and taking your time to get to the D. This is done by continuing the ritardando through the first beat of bar 62. Then return to the exact tempo for the triplet run and pause slightly on the trilled F sharp. Take the low B in the left hand in time. The reason for not using a termination on this trill is so that it will not interfere with the low B. Use four notes only for the trill and play them very quickly holding the last F sharp.

THE SCHOLAR'S SCARLATTI
VOLUME THREE

Edited by
Stoddard Lincoln

Domenico SCARLATTI
(1685 - 1757)

a. [Set 1; E major]
31. K.162; L.121

6

32. K.163; L.63

Set 2 in F Minor

33. K. 185 (L. 173)

This austere sonata is excellent for practising long phrases with rests in them. The right hand of the opening phrase consists of minims followed by minim rests. The fingering is immaterial as no legato is required but the line must be kept by the constantly-rising wrist. Guard against relaxing the wrist during the rests.

The left hand too must be one long phrase but with a rather more complicated articulation. Make a tiny articulation between the two F's of the octave leap and take the dot, as usual, as a rest. In order to measure the articulation of the octave leap look at bar 20 where the leap is a seventh and taken from the 5th finger to the 2nd. The fingering creates an articulation. Observe the time you take for that articulation and apply the same amount of time for the articulation in all of the octave leaps.

Not only are all the dots in the piece to be read as rests but also the second note of a tie should be treated as a rest.

bb 16 & 23 The accidentals in the original create the leap of an augmented second on the last beat of these two bars. This is inconsistent with the many other times this figure is used, hence the editorial suggestions for altering the accidentals in order to avoid the augmented second.

bb 49–53 By gradually introducing steady quavers in the right hand Scarlatti brings the sonata to a climax. Highlight the high C in bar 52 by using some rubato in this passage.

The second ending and final cadence require four full beats before going on or taking the repeat. This is a long time and you might want to fill out the two bars in question as was frequently done in actual performance. In this case the addition of appoggiaturas will work very well. On the second ending take a two-beat double appoggiatura using the B and D natural of the previous measure. In the final bar take a minim E-natural appoggiatura the first time around and no appoggiatura for the final cadence.

34. K. 184 (L. 189)

This very Spanish-sounding sonata depends more on a heavily-accented first beat than it does on a quick tempo.

bb 9–18 This figure of a semiquaver rest followed by five semiquavers and then a bar of three quavers or a dotted crotchet accompanied by repeated notes in the left hand is scattered throughout the sonata. Take the first bar in a steady tempo but, in the second, hold the first quaver slightly. This will give you time to leap to the trill on the second beat and make the articulation marked in the score.

bb 29–34 This is a very difficult passage to finger because of the accidentals but this fingering will work as well as any. 'Block' it as chords several times. In getting to the last note (b 30, beat 3) keep your hand level but turn it slightly to the right from the wrist. This will move your thumb naturally to the E flat and in turn place your little finger over the C. Prepare the fermata with a healthy ritardando which you might find most welcome because of the awkwardness of the passage and the fact that you have to play it accurately three times in a row. The parallel passage in the second half, fortunately, is not quite as difficult as Scarlatti mercifully leaves out the double note.

bb 69–77 Notice the extended use of the hemiola here and at the parallel place at the crux. The fingering is designed to accent it clearly.

b. [Set 2; F minor]

33. K.185; L.173

34. K.184; L.189

Set 3 in D Major
35. K. 277 (L. 183)

This elegant sonata with its ornate melody of varied rhythms and wide leaps is typical of the *style galant*. The form is interesting in that there is no crux, but rather a free working out of the opening motif. The return of the initial material at bar 32, which rounds out the form, is so cleverly disguised that one might easily miss it. Bar 32 is different from the opening but bar 33 is the same as bar 2. Bars 34 and 35 are a melodic variation of bars 3 and 4 cast over the same left hand. The piece then continues freely to its final cadence.

b 3 Scarlatti is very precise about these appoggiaturas as he writes them out as semiquavers and dotted quavers. Popular towards the end of the Baroque era, this is known as a Lombard rhythm, identical to the Scotch snap. The acciaccatura on the third beat must be distinguished from it: play it a little shorter than a semiquaver.

b 12 Notice the use of the third finger on the low A to keep the wrist up for the phrase ending. If you really want more of a legato in the left hand take the G sharp of the second beat with your right hand and only the E with your left.

b 22 Substituting the 5th finger for the thumb on the second beat is awkward, but it is necessary in order to get the thumb down to the C sharp on the next beat. In making the substitution you will discover that you tend to touch the A on the second beat quickly and lightly with your 4th finger just before placing the 5th finger on it. Experiment with this and observe what your 4th finger does carefully. It will help to get your hand into a better position.

b 31 The only way to keep a smooth line here is to take the upper auxiliary of the trill on the second beat (D) with the thumb, cross over to the C quickly with the second finger and then execute the remainder of the trill with the second and third fingers. Because the lyric nature of this piece calls for 'Vocal' trills which linger on the first note and gradually accelerate, such a fingering is possible.

b 38 The beautiful 4/2 chord on the first beat can be brought out by rolling it from the beat and bringing the E of the melody in as the last member of the chord. Make a ritardando up to the climactic high B to get it 'over the hump'.

b 38 The C sharp on the second beat is unusual, to say the least, and takes some getting used to. Even though a B is harmonically more 'correct', the C sharp is typical of Scarlatti. I leave the choice up to you.

36. K. 282 (L. 484)

This sonata is even more irregular in its form with its two interpolations of extraneous material. The interpolation of the minuet-like section in the second part is obvious because of the change in mode, tempo and metre. The interpolation in the first part is not quite as noticeable (bb 15 – 31) but it is clearly set off by fermatas. Without these interpolations the piece would be perfectly regular (if not dull).

If you repeat the second section of this sonata you will find that the mood of the *minuet* becomes so prevalent that the overall brilliance of the work is snuffed out. Consider omitting this repeat.

bb 10 – 11 The leap down to the A in the left hand is tricky. You will find that the passage is more easy to play at tempo than slowly.

bb 15 – 31 Begin this passage a little under tempo and bring it back up to speed at bar 21. Harpsichordists might wish to take this on two keyboards in order to cut down the racket of the repeated-chord accompaniment. That Scarlatti conceived it for one keyboard is seen in bars 16, 18 and 20 where he leaves out upper notes in the chords so that the melody will not collide with them.

bb 96 – 98 Watch your left hand thumb here. The articulation invites playing it on the second beat, not the first as Scarlatti writes it.

c. [Set 3; D major]

35. K.277; L.183

Cantabile andantino

36. K. 282; L.484

Andante ♩=♩

Set 4 in A Major

37. K. 268 (L. 41)

This spacious sonata is rich in its variety of material. Bars 15–27 are of particular interest because of their harmonic structure. Notice the insistence of the B-major chord in bars 15 and 16. What a surprise when it veers off to the G major arpeggio in bar 18! Then Scarlatti takes another thrust from B major only to wind up equally unexpectedly in A minor (b 22)! Where is he going? The last bout takes us where he wants us – B major – just where we were the whole time. At this point he settles down to ordinary progressions for the close of the half.

Not only does Scarlatti play with the harmonies but he also plays with the rhythm: each one of these outbursts is surrounded by fermatas which takes them out of the main time-stream of the sonata. Be sure to give the fermatas plenty of extra time. They take more than you think – sit on your hands for a minute then go on.

The next appearance of these chords is right after the double bar where one would expect some sort of a harmonic exploration. But no – here Scarlatti sits right on the C sharp major chord without budging, and then begins the exploration with material taken from the first phrase. The last appearance of this passage is like the first but transposed to E major.

38. K. 62 (L. 45)

This robust dance depends on a very strong downbeat.

bb 7–9 You can add brilliance to this passage by playing a long trill for these two bars. The trick is to stop the trill in time to play the A of bar 9 clearly. Take the trill through the first two beats of bar 8, stopping it without a termination very precisely on the third beat. This will clear the air for the final A.

bb 26–31 Take the D-sharp acciaccatura with the thumb, playing it simultaneously with the low E. Quickly slide the thumb off of it to the E so you smash the whole thing at the same time. The effect should be brutal.

bb 49–51 This cadential flourish and the one that terminates the piece are problems because they do not add up rhythmically. I think that Scarlatti's intention is to release the tremendous energy of the sonata by a sort of whiplash. You can achieve the effect by flourishing the final scale as quickly as you possibly can, forgetting the pulse. Some sources give only a sustained bass note under the run as is seen in the final bar. Start practising with the sustained note until you work up maximum speed. Then, if you wish, place the repeated bass notes where they appear visually in relationship to the scales, letting the scale be your guide, not the repeated notes. If you do this at the first half also do it for the final ending as I have indicated by the notes in the brackets.

bb 52–57 This alternation of hands is a great favourite of Scarlatti's. In the first two bars if the stems go up they are for the right hand and if they go down they are for the left hand. Place the right hand over the left hand and use a very sharp staccato so that you will be off the note in time for the other hand to strike it.

Bars 54–56 are as Scarlatti wrote them. In order to keep up the brilliance, divide the descent between the hands as you did the ascent. If the fingering is above the notes use your right hand; if it is below use your left hand. As the right hand leads up so the left hand leads down. The easiest way to make this shift is to take the first two notes of bar 54 with the right hand as the placement of the fingering suggests.

bb 62–65 Yes, these chords are correct. Scarlatti is noted for such dissonances and the effect is stunning.

b 86 The original source gives A and F natural for the second beat. This destroys the whole sequence.

b 98 The trill is impossible. Ignore it! If you do want to fool around with it try an acciaccatura on the D above, but you will still get into hot water. Let sleeping dogs lie!

bb 99–103 This return of the opening flourish is sheer noise. If you want to add to the clatter, trill the left hand continuously for bars 100–102. But stop the trill on the first beat of 103 so that the C sharp of the next measure can be clearly heard.

d. [Set 4; A major]
37. K.268; L.41

38. K.62; L.45

Set 5 in D Minor
39. K. 213 (L. 108)
This sonata is the essence of Spanish tragedy: proud but never pathetic.

bb 6—10 At such a slow tempo one can logically argue that each bar here is a phrase. By all means start practising it that way until you get the grand gesture. After that, try the phrasing indicated in order to keep the music moving. The logic behind the phrasing is that the first three bars make up a descending sequence and the next two are a repetition of each other. The same logic has been applied to the similar passage in the second half (bb 30—39) which also begins with a descending sequence which makes up the first phrase. The next three phrases each consist of one bar which is repeated.

bb 36—39 Although Scarlatti uses a trill for the right-hand ornament in each bar here, I recommend a mordent. Therefore, the **3-2** fingering does not mean that you take a short trill from the upper auxiliary but rather place the 3rd finger on the written note and go down a step and back up for a mordent. It fits in very nicely with the short trill beginning on the principal note in the left hand.

bb 49—50 The octaves have been fingered here to ensure a legato. If your hand is too small use **5-1** for them, but stay as close to the keys as you can and let your ascending wrist keep the line.

40. K. 191 (L. 207)
Whatever the tragedy was of the previous sonata, this petulant piece certainly wreaks its revenge on it. Try taking both repeats as doing so will increase your endurance.

bb 59—63 The hemiola here has been indicated by the articulation marks in the left hand rather than brackets which would span too great a space to be practical.

bb 74—75 It was common practice for the player to supply bridges at the two main cadences leading back to repeats if the pause seemed too long. Scarlatti supplies such bridges for the first and second endings of the first half but none for the first ending of the second half. Such a long rest kills the momentum and excitement of the sonata, so I have suggested a bridge for the left hand in brackets.

e. [Set 5; D minor]

39. K.213; L.108

40. K.191; L.207

Set 6 in E Minor

41. K. 263 (L. 321)

One of Scarlatti's most profound sonatas, the opening invokes an almost religious feeling with its brief counterpoint and suspensions. In order not to set too quick a tempo think of the tempo you want for the semiquaver passages beginning in bar 20 and hear those notes in your mind as you play the opening bars.

bb 6 – 12 Work out the fingering for these double notes carefully. When conquered it will yield a good legato.

bb 20 – 24 The runs in the right hand lie very awkwardly, hence the many contractions. They seem to fit the left hand more comfortably.

bb 28 – 29 Try breaking some of the left-hand chords in this passage whenever it appears. The chord on the second beat of bar 28 sounds well broken as it comes between the syncopation in the right hand and will stretch the beat slightly. It is not necessary to break the next chord but, if you do, break it more quickly than the one on the second beat.

In bar 40 break either the first or the second right-hand chord. In the closing three bars breaking all the chords will sound messy so choose the most important. To begin with, try breaking the right-hand chord in bar 74 and the left-hand chord on the last beat of the next measure. Be sure to break them from the beat, not before it.

Generally speaking, when you have a series of chords do not break them all and vary the speed at which you break them. In lyric pieces, the more slowly you break a chord the more emphasis it is given, so choose the most dissonant ones. Experiment and listen to the results.

bb 34 – 39 Play all the semiquavers as melody, not just figuration. Here and in similar passages experiment with rubato so that the semiquavers will not sound mechanical.

Both hands take the D on the second beat of bar 38. The two thumbs will fit, so don't worry. If you want, you could leave out the left hand and D but this will jeopardize the smoothness of the line.

bb 58 – 62 The articulations are different in each hand in order to bring out the imitative counterpoint. Practise the hands separately until each feels comfortable with the articulation and will maintain its individuality when put against the other.

42. K. 233 (L. 467)

Despite the *allegro* tempo marking pathos lies very close to the surface of this subdued sonata. It must be played smoothly with an emphasis on its lyricism rather than brilliance.

bb 1 – 15 Repeated notes work best moving from the little finger towards the thumb and are quite awkward moving the other way. Therefore repeated notes are advised in the right hand but not the left.

However tempting it may be, do not slur the third of the repeated notes to the next beat. This would sound particularly vulgar in the upward leaps of a sixth beginning in bar 9. Play the repeated notes as closely together as you can and take that amount of space for the leap to the first beat of the next measure.

18 – 22 Even though Scarlatti scores the D for both hands take it with the left hand only or you will get tangled up.

bb 27 – 32 Baroque composers frequently imply two-voice writing in a single melodic line, and such is the case in these bars. Practise them as in example 2 in order to bring out the contrapuntal implications. In the phrase that parallels this in the second part (bb 100 – 104) Scarlatti actually uses two voices.

EXAMPLE 2

bb 50–56   At this tempo it is necessary to change fingers on repeated notes. Be careful not to dip the wrist for each beat or you will jam. Use only a finger action, quickly releasing the second semiquaver of each beat so that it can be replaced by the different finger on the same note for the next beat. Use the wrist to define the phrase.

bb 59–70   Notice how carefully Scarlatti indicates the hemiola here and the finger-pedalling of the bass notes. The cross rhythms in bars 66–69 are even more fascinating. The ascending-scale figure takes four beats, as is indicated by the articulation signs, but the bass moves on steadily in the basic triplet rhythm.

bb 156–159   The last three bars are extremely troublesome because of the plunge to middle C and the quick harmonic rhythm of the antepenultimate bar. 'Blocking' it as chords helps tremendously.

f. [Set 6; E minor]
41. K. 263; L. 321

42. K.233; L.467

George Frideric Handel

TWENTY OVERTURES IN AUTHENTIC KEYBOARD ARRANGEMENTS
Edited in three volumes by **Terence Best**

This highly important issue forms the first publication of Handel's own arrangements of 20 of his operatic overtures for keyboard. These constitute a substantial addition to the repertoire of both professionals and amateurs alike. This edition, by the leading Handel scholar in this field, contains detailed notes on sources and performance.

Review "His [*Terence Best*] Preface is masterly and the presentation of the music demonstrates the scrupulous care which has gone into this edition . . . . . They are all for manuals only and will make a tremendous addition to the organist's impoverished repertoire of Handel's organ music."

Organists' Review

VOLUME ONE

Il Pastor Fido I & II
Teseo
Amadigi
Esther

VOLUME TWO

Radamisto
Muzio Scevola
Ottone
Flavio
Giulio Cesare
Tamerlano
Rodelinda
Scipione
Alessandro

VOLUME THREE

Admeto I & II
Riccardo Primo
Lotario
Partenope
Orlando
Semele

Photograph of portrait of Handel by Mercier   © The Viscount Fitzharris.